Antonio Soler

14 SONATAS

Antonio Soler

14 SONATAS

from the Fitzwilliam Collection

Edited by

KENNETH GILBERT

1987

FABER MUSIC LIMITED

LONDON

© 1987 by Faber Music Ltd
First published 1987 by Faber Music Ltd
3 Queen Square London WC1N 3AU
French translation by Maurice Decker
German translation by Helga Braun
Printed in England by Halstan & Co. Ltd
Music set by Musicpage
Cover design by M & S Tucker
The facsimiles on p. ix are reproduced by kind permission
of the Syndics of the Fitzwilliam Museum

CONTENTS · TABLE · INHALT

PREFACE

Padre Antonio Soler (1729–1783) has been overshadowed, understandably but perhaps unfairly, by the towering personality of Domenico Scarlatti. His total known output as a keyboard composer – 120 sonatas in the Rubio catalogue to date – amounts to less than a quarter of Scarlatti's production. However, Soler also left a sizable amount of vocal music, both religious and secular, as well as liturgical organ works, a set of six quintets with keyboard obbligato, a further set of six *conciertos* for two keyboard instruments, and a number of theoretical writings. This makes him one of the most important musical figures of 18th-century Spain. Far from being a mere imitator of his more illustrious contemporary, Soler as a composer shows considerable originality and points the way towards the final development of the harpsichord idiom, even to a point of confluence with the emerging pianoforte style. He shares with Scarlatti and other Spanish composers a fondness for the characteristic dance rhythms and the harmonic-melodic features of Iberian popular music.

This edition offers a selection of 14 sonatas from the set of 27 which was printed in London, in or before 1796, by the publisher Robert Birchall. It was to be the only publication of Soler's sonatas before the 20th century, when Joaquín Nin and Roberto Gerhard sparked the revival that led to the publication of the bulk of the composer's keyboard music in editions by Kastner, Marvin and Rubio (the Birchall sonatas correspond to the first 27 of Rubio's collected edition).

The title-page reads: *XXVII Sonatas Para Clave Por el Padre Fray Antonio Soler, Que ha Impresso Roberto Birchall, Nº 133, New Bond Street* [no date]. A copy in the Fitzwilliam Museum, Cambridge, on which the present edition is based, is signed and dated 'Fitzwilliam 1796'. It belonged to Richard, Viscount Fitzwilliam (1745–1816), the eminent collector and music-lover who had met Soler on a visit to Spain in 1772. An inscription on the front fly-leaf tells the story: 'These lessons for the harpsichord were given to Lord Fitzwilliam in manuscript in February, 1772, by Father Soler, the author, of the convent of Ieronomites at the palace of the Escurial.–' On the *verso* of the fly-leaf: 'The originals of these harpsichord lessons were given to me by Father Soler, at the Escurial, the 14ᵗʰ February, 1772. Fitzwᵐ. Father Soler had been instructed by Scarlatti.–' Six copies of this edition are known to have survived. (On the same occasion Fitzwilliam received several manuscript scores of sonatas by Domenico Scarlatti, Soler's sometime teacher; these were also to be published later by Birchall.)

27 seems an odd number for a collection which, in the composer's mind, could well have been intended for publication in London. Sets of 30 pieces seem to have been fairly common at the time – Scarlatti's *Essercizi*, published in London in 1738, and the Venice manuscripts of Scarlatti and Albero come to mind. It is tempting to speculate that from an original set of 30, three sonatas may have been lost at some point during the 25 years or so that elapsed before their publication. In any case the entire manuscript is now considered lost; it has never been part of the Fitzwilliam Museum collections and was quite possibly discarded once the work was in print, a standard practice at the time (although the Scarlatti manuscripts were returned to Fitzwilliam by the printer and thus can now be compared with the printed version).

The paired arrangement favoured by Scarlatti, Albero and many other Spanish and Italian composers of the period is present here also, although not in systematic fashion. Of the 27 sonatas, 20 appear to have been arranged in pairs, and these include the possibility of two triptychs. Five of these pairs have been included in the present selection (Nos. 3–4, 7–8, 9–10, 11–12 and 13–14).

Considering the rising importance of the fortepiano during the final decades of the century, and the fact that instruments of this type are known to have been in use in Madrid, it seems highly likely that the sonatas would have been performed on either harpsichord or fortepiano. The recurring use of the high G, hardly ever found on surviving harpsichords of the period, certainly points in the direction of an expanded keyboard such as might have been encountered on later Iberian instruments. There is a high A on a 1789 harpsichord with two eight-foot registers by Antunes in Lisbon, but the mystery surrounding the high G in Soler's sonatas remains as great as it is with other contemporary Spanish composers such as Scarlatti, Albero and Blasco de Nebra. Significantly, in the 18th century, English 5-octave spinets frequently had the high G, and part of the answer could lie in this direction. These large-size spinets seem to have been in considerable demand as domestic keyboard instruments, both in England and abroad. They are surprisingly powerful in tone, and it would be modern prejudice, conditioned by present-day concert habits, to imagine that such an instrument would have been incapable of doing justice in most instances to the textures and expressive demands of the Scarlatti and Soler 'lessons', simply because it had only one eight-foot register.

Ornaments are indicated in the Birchall print by the sign *tr*; this is probably meant to represent either a trill with the upper auxiliary note or, occasionally, a lower mordent, depending on the context (there are also a few mordent signs, inconsistently placed). As I have stated in the preface to my edition of the sonatas of Scarlatti, there are good reasons for believing that the trill in 18th-century Spanish music usually begins on the main note, unless an upper note is specifically indicated by a small appoggiatura. This solution seems to make the most sense in a vast majority of cases, but the performer may feel free to begin a trill on the upper note if the context seems to call for it. Both types of trill were part of the musical vocabulary of the period, and it would be unwise to maintain the view – held until recently – that all trills, long or short, began on the upper note as a matter of principle.

The original print abounds in errors of every kind, from missing or misplaced accidentals to wrong notes and chords. The text was clearly never properly proof-read. In preparing this selection, I have accounted for most of these misprints in the Editorial Notes. Obvious errors, mainly concerning ties and about which there could be no possible doubt, have been corrected without mention; in more questionable cases I have felt it necessary to explain my choices. Soler's musical intentions, however, are almost always perfectly clear.

A small number of obviously indispensable ornaments have been extrapolated from parallel passages; these are listed separately and can be easily marked into the text as editorial, should the player feel it necessary. Occasional notes, ties, slurs and accidentals have been added where the evidence of earlier parallel passages in the same piece indicates that they are obviously missing; these have not been identified by means of the usual scholarly apparatus. My concern throughout has been to present the cleanest possible text, ready for performance and unencumbered with visual editorial interference in the form of brackets, marked slurs and ties, and similar devices which can often be distracting to the player. Thus, the concise Editorial Notes need only be deciphered once and for all for each sonata, with pencil in hand.

I am grateful to the Syndics of the Fitzwilliam Museum, Cambridge, for permission to publish this anthology from their copy of the original print.

Chartres, 1986   KENNETH GILBERT

PRÉFACE

Le Père Antonio Soler (1729–1783) a été éclipsé, de façon compréhensible mais peut-être injuste, par la personalité dominante de Domenico Scarlatti. Pour le seul clavier, l'oeuvre connu (120 sonates au catalogue Rubio à ce jour) représente à peine le quart de celui de Scarlatti. Cependant, Soler nous a légué quantité de musique vocale, tant religieuse que profane, ainsi que des oeuvres liturgiques pour orgue, un ensemble de six quintettes pour clavier obbligato, un autre ensemble de six *conciertos* pour deux claviers, et une somme considérable d'écrits théoriques. Ce qui fait de lui l'une des figures les plus marquantes de l'Espagne musicale du 18e siècle. Loin de n'être qu'un simple disciple de son compatriote plus illustre, le compositeur Soler démontre une originalité considérable et ouvre la voie du développement final du langage propre au clavecin, jusqu'au point où celui-ci se confond avec le style alors naissant du piano-forte. Il partage avec Scarlatti et d'autres compositeurs espagnols un goût marqué pour la rythmique des danses et pour les caractéristiques harmoniques et mélodiques de la musique populaire ibérique.

Cette édition offre une sélection de 14 sonates choisies parmi les 27 qui furent imprimées à Londres, avant ou pendant l'année 1796, par l'éditeur Robert Birchall. Ce devait être la seule publication des sonates de Soler jusqu'au 20e siècle, lorsque Joaquín Nin et Roberto Gerhard furent à l'origine d'un regain d'intérêt pour la musique de Soler, ce qui conduisit à la publication de la presque totalité de l'oeuvre pour clavier dans des éditions dues à Kastner, Marvin et Rubio (les 27 sonates de Birchall correspondant aux 27 premières de l'édition groupée de Rubio).

La page de titre indique: *XXVII Sonatas Para Clave Por el Padre Fray Antonio Soler, Que ha Impresso Roberto Birchall, Nº 133, New Bond Street* [sans date]. Il existe au Fitzwilliam Museum de Cambridge un exemplaire ainsi libellé 'Fitzwilliam 1796'; c'est sur lui que repose la présente édition. Il fut la propriété de Richard, Viscount Fitzwilliam (1745–1816), l'éminent collectionneur et mélomane qui rencontra Soler lors d'un séjour en Espagne en 1772. Sur la page de garde figure la précision suivante: 'Ces leçons pour le clavecin ont été données à Lord Fitzwilliam sous forme de manuscrit en février 1772 par l'auteur, le Père Soler, du couvent des Hieronomites, au palais de l'Escorial.–' Et au verso: 'Les originaux de ces leçons pour clavecin m'ont été donnés par le Père Soler, à l'Escorial, le 14 février 1772. Fitzwᵐ. Le Père Soler avait reçu l'enseignement de Scarlatti.–' De cette édition on connait aujourd'hui six exemplaires. A cette occasion, Fitzwilliam se vit également confier plusieurs partitions manuscrites de Domenico Scarlatti, qui fut un temps le maître de Soler; elles aussi devaient être publiées plus tard par Birchall.

27 peut sembler un nombre curieux pour un ensemble que l'auteur pourrait bien avoir envisagé de faire publier à Londres. Des ensembles de 30 sonates semblent avoir été plutôt courants à l'époque – on songe aux *Essercizi* de Scarlatti, édités à Londres en 1738, ainsi qu'aux manuscrits vénitiens de Scarlatti et d'Albero. Il est tentant de se dire que, d'une série originale de 30 sonates, trois ont pu être perdues au cours des quelques 25 années qui se sont écoulées avant leur publication. Quoi qu'il en soit, le manuscrit entier est aujourd'hui considéré comme perdu; il n'a jamais fait partie des collections du Fitzwilliam Museum et a très probablement été détruit une fois l'impression terminée, pratique courante à l'époque (et ce, bien que les manuscrits de Scarlatti aient été renvoyés par l'imprimeur et puissent ainsi être comparés avec la version imprimée).

L'arrangement par couples, privilégié par Scarlatti, Albero et de nombreux autres musiciens espagnols et italiens du 18e siècle, se retrouve également ici, mais pas de façon systématique. Sur les 27 sonates, 20 semblent avoir été arrangées par couples, y compris la possibilité de deux triptyques. La présente édition inclut cinq de ces couples (nos. 3–4, 7–8, 9–10, 11–12 et 13–14).

Si l'on considère l'importance croissante du piano-forte pendant les dernières décades du siècle, et le fait que des instruments de ce type sont connus comme ayant été en usage à Madrid, il est probable que les sonates ont été jouées sans distinction au clavecin comme au piano-forte. L'utilisation fréquente du Sol aigu, rarement présent sur les instruments de l'époque ayant survécu, nous incline à envisager un clavier 'étendu', comme il a pu en exister sur des instruments espagnols plus tardifs. On trouve un La aigu sur un clavecin comportant deux jeux d'unisson, fait par Antunes à Lisbonne en 1789, mais le mystère qui entoure la présence du Sol aigu dans les sonates de Soler demeure entier, qu'il s'agisse de Soler d'ailleurs, ou de Scarlatti, Albero, et Blasco de Nebra. Fait important, les épinettes anglaises comportant cinq octaves présentent fréquemment ce Sol aigu, et je pense qu'une partie de la réponse pourrait bien venir de cette direction. Ces grandes épinettes semblent avoir été fort prisées en tant qu'instruments à usage privé, en Angleterre comme à l'étranger. Ils sonts étonnamment puissants pour ce qui est du son lui-même, et ce serait faire preuve d'un préjugé moderne, conditionné par les actuelles normes de nos salles de concerts, que d'imaginer un tel instrument incapable de rendre justice, dans la plupart des cas, à l'écriture et aux exigences expressives auxquelles font appel les 'leçons' de Scarlatti et de Soler, pour l'unique raison qu'il ne possède qu'un seul registre.

Les ornements, dans l'édition Birchall, sont indiqués par le signe *tr*; ceci, probablement pour représenter un trille avec la note supérieure, ou, occasionellement, un mordant inférieur, selon le contexte (on trouve aussi quelques signes de mordant placés ici ou là). Comme je l'ai déjà établi dans ma préface à l'édition des sonates de Scarlatti, il existe de bonnes raisons pour penser que le trille dans l'Espagne du 18e siècle commence généralement sur la note réelle, à moins qu'une petite appoggiature ne vienne indiquer spécifiquement la note supérieure. Cette solution semble être la bonne dans la majorité des cas, mais l'interprète doit évidemment se sentir libre de commencer sur la note supérieure si le contexte semble l'exiger. Le vocabulaire musical de l'époque admettait les deux sortes de trilles, et il ne serait pas raisonnable de s'en tenir à l'idée (en vigueur jusqu'à récemment) selon laquelle, longs ou courts, tous les trilles doivent être amorcés par principe par la note supérieure.

L'édition originale abonde en erreurs de toutes sortes: altérations mal placées ou manquantes, notes et accords incorrects, etc... Il est clair que les épreuves n'ont jamais été corrigées. Lors de la réalisation de cette anthologie, j'ai traité de ces erreurs dans l'appareil critique. Les fautes les plus flagrantes, surtout celles concernant les liaisons absentes, ont été corrigées sans qu'il en soit fait mention; seuls les cas douteux ont fait l'objet d'explications. De toute façon, dans la presque totalité des cas, les intentions musicales de Soler ne laissent aucun doute.

Quelques ornements, dont il est manifeste qu'ils sont indispensables, ont été déduits logiquement de passages similaires. On en trouvera une liste détaillée; l'interprète qui le jugerait utile pourra toujours les noter sur la partition. Lorsqu'un passage précédent indique clairement leur absence, altérations, liaisons, tenues et notes occasionelles ont été ajoutées; celles-ci n'ont pas été identifiées par les signes musicologiques usuels. Mon souci constant a été de présenter le texte le plus clair possible, sans l'adjonction d'interventions visibles sour forme de crochets, liaisons et tenues barrées et autres signes qui peuvent distraire inutilement l'interprète. Ainsi, les notes de l'éditeur, volontairement succinctes, ne nécessiteront qu'une seule lecture pour chaque sonate, crayon en main.

Je suis reconnaissant aux Conservateurs du Fitzwilliam Museum, Cambridge, pour l'autorisation de publier cette anthologie d'après leur exemplaire original.

Chartres, 1986   KENNETH GILBERT

VORWORT

Verständlicher, aber vielleicht doch unberechtigterweise stand Padre Antonio Soler (1729–1783) im Schatten der überragenden Persönlichkeit Domenico Scarlattis. Sein gesamtes bekanntes Werk als Komponist für Tasteninstrumente – 120 Sonaten im Rubio Katalog bisher – beträgt weniger als ein viertel der Produktion Scarlattis. Soler hinterließ ebenfalls eine beträchtliche Menge an sowohl religiöser als auch weltlicher Gesangsmusik, wie auch liturgische Orgelwerke, einen Satz von sechs Quintetten mit Klavier-Obbligato, ein weiterer Satz von sechs Konzerten für zwei Tasteninstrumente und eine Anzahl wichtiger theoretischer Schriften. Dies macht ihn zu einem der wichtigsten spanischen Musiker des 18. Jahrhunderts. Weit entfernt davon, einfach ein Imitator seines berühmten Landsmannes zu sein, zeigt Soler als Komponist beträchtliche Originalität und weist den Weg zur weiteren Entwicklung der Cembalotechnik bis hin zum Zusammenfluß mit dem aufkommenden Klavier. Was er mit Scarlatti und anderen spanischen Komponisten gemeinsam hat, ist die Vorliebe für die charakteristischen Tanzrhythmen und die harmonisch-melodischen Eigenheiten der iberischen volkstümlichen Musik.

Diese Ausgabe bietet eine Auswahl von 14 Sonaten aus dem Satz von 27, der vor 1796 von dem Verleger Robert Birchall in London gedruckt wurde. Dieses sollte die einzige Veröffentlichung von Solers Sonaten bis zum 20. Jahrhundert bleiben, bis Joqauín Nin und Roberto Gerhard den Funken zur Wiederbelebung entzündeten, der zur Publikation eines großen Teils der Tasteninstrumentenmusik des Komponisten führten in Ausgaben von Kastner, Marvin und Rubio (die Birchall Sonaten entsprechen den ersten 27 der gesammelten Ausgabe von Rubio).

Auf der Titelseite heißt es: *XXVII Sonatas Para Clave Por el Padre Fray Antonio Soler, Que ha Impresso Roberto Birchall, N° 133, New Bond Street* [ohne Datum]. Eine Kopie im Fitzwilliam Museum, Cambridge, auf die sich die gegenwärtige Ausgabe stüzt, trägt als Unterschrift und Datum 'Fitzwilliam 1796'. Sie gehörte dem Vicomte Richard Fitzwilliam (1745–1816), einem hervorragenden Sammler und Musikliebhaber, der Soler bei einem Besuch in Spanien im Jahre 1772 kennengelernt hatte. Eine Inschrift auf dem vorderen Deckblatt erzählt die Geschichte: 'Diese Übungsstücke für Cembalo wurden Lord Fitzwilliam als Handschrift von dem Verfasser, Vater Soler im Kloster der Ieronomiten im Escorial Palast übergeben.–' Auf der andere Seite des Deckblatts heißt es: 'Die Originale dieser Cembalo-Übungsstücke wurden mir am 14. Februar von Vater Soler im Escorial gegeben. Fitzw^m. Vater Soler war ein Schuler Scarlattis.–' Soweit bekannt, existieren noch sechs Kopien dieser Ausgabe. (Zur gleichen Gelegenheit erhielt Fitzwilliam mehrere Manuskriptpartituren von Sonaten Domenico Scarlattis, der zeitweise Solers Lehrer war; diese wurden ebenfalls später von Birchall herausgegeben.)

27 scheint eine merkwürdige Zahl zu sein für eine Sammlung, die, nach Vorstellung des Komponisten, sehr wohl für die Veröffentlichung in London gedacht gewesen sein könnte. Sätze von 30 Stücken scheinen damals ziemlich normal gewesen zu sein – hier fallen einem Scarlattis *Essercizi*, 1738 in London veröffentlicht, und die Venedig-Manuskripte von Scarlatti und Albero ein. Es bietet sich die überlegung an, daß drei der 30 Sonaten des Originalsatzes irgendwann während der 25 Jahre oder mehr, die bis zur Veröffentlichung verstrichen, verloren gingen. Auf jeden Fall gilt heute das Gesamtmanuskript als verloren; es war zu keinem Zeitpunkt Bestandteil der Sammlungen des Fitzwilliam Museums, und es ist durchaus möglich, daß es, sobald das Werk gedruckt war, weggeworfen wurde, was der Praxis der Zeit entsprach (obwohl Scarlattis Manuskripte vom Drucker an Fitzwilliam zurückgeschickt wurden und somit heute mit der gedruckten Version verglichen werden können).

Das paarweise angelegte Arrangement, das von Scarlatti, Albero und vielen anderen spanischen und italienischen Komponisten mit Vorliebe gewählt wurde, ist hier ebenfalls gegeben, wenn auch nicht in systematischer Ordnung. 20 der 27 Sonaten scheinen paarweise angelegt worden zu sein, und diese schließen die Möglichkeit von zwei Tryptichonen ein. Fünf dieser Paare sind mit in die gegen-wärtige Auswahl aufgenommen worden (Nr. 3–4, 7–8, 9–10, 11–12 und 13–14).

In Anbetracht der wachsenden Wichtigkeit des Fortepiano während der letzten Jahrzehnts des Jahrhundert, und in Anbetracht der Tatsache, daß Instrumente von diesem Typus in Madrid benutzt wurden, scheint es sehr warhscheinlich, daß die Sonaten entweder auf dem Cembalo oder dem Fortepiano gespielt wurden. Der wiederholte Gebrauch des hohen G, das sonst kaum auf irgendeinem der Cembalos der Zeit zu finden ist, deutet sicherlich auf eine erweiterte Tastatur hin, so wie man sie vielleicht auf späteren iberischen Instrumenten hätte finden können. Es gibt ein hohes A auf einem Cembalo mit zwei acht-Fuß Registern aus dem Jahre 1789 von Antunes in Lissabon, aber das Geheimnis des hohen G in Solers Sonaten bleibt ebenso myseriös wie bei anderen zeitgenössischen spanischen Komponisten wie Scarlatti, Albero und Blasco de Nebra. Bezeichnenderweise hatten englische 5-Oktaven Spinette häufig das hohe G, und die Antwort liegt wohl teilweise in dieser Richtung. Die Nachfrage nach großen Spinetten als private Tasteninstrumente muß, sowohl in England als auch im Ausland, beträchtlich gewesen sein. Sie haben einen erstaunlich kraftvollen Klang, und es entspräche einem modernen Vorurteil, bedingt durch heutige Konzertgewohnheiten, anzunehmen, daß solch ein Instrument normalerweise nicht in der Lage gewesen sein sollte, dem Gefüge und den Ausdrucksanforderungen der Übungsstücke Scarlattis und Solers gerecht zu werden, einfach weil es nur ein acht-Fuß Register hatte.

Verziehrungen sind im Birchall-Druck mit *tr* bezeichnet; dieses zeigt wahrscheinlich entweder einen Triller mit oberer Hilfsnote an oder gelegentlich, vom Zusammenhang bedingt, einen Mordent nach unten (es gibt ebenfalls einige wenige, willkürlich gesetzte Mordentzeichen). Im Vorwort zu meiner Ausgabe von Scarlattis Sonaten habe ich gesagt, daß es gute Gründe gibt, anzunehmen, daß der Triller in der spanischen Musik des 18. Jahrhunderts in den meisten Fällen auf der Hauptnote beginnt, wenn nicht ausdrücklich ein höhere Note von einer kleinen Appoggiatura angezeigt ist. Diese Lösung scheint in der Mehrzahl aller Fälle die sinnvollste zu sein, aber es muß natürlich nicht extra gesagt werden, daß es dem Spieler freisteht, einen Triller auf der oberen Note zu beginnen, wenn dies vom Zusammenhang aus besser erscheint. Beide Trillerarten waren ein Teil des musikalischen Vokabulars der Zeit, und es wäre unsinnig, die Ansicht aufrecht erhalten zu wollen – wie bis noch vor einiger Zeit geschehen – daß alle Triller, lange oder kurze, grundsätzlich auf der oberen Note begannen.

Der Originaldruck wimmelt von Fehlern jeder Art, angefangen von fehlenden oder falsch gesetzten Vorzeichen, bis hin zu falschen Noten und Akkorden. Ganz offensichtlich ist der Text niemals gründlich korrekturgelesen worden. Bei der Vorbereitung dieser Auswahl habe ich die meisten Fehldrucke in den Herausgeberanmerkungen aufgeführt. Offensichtliche Fehler, die hauptsächlich die Bindungen betreffen und keinerlei Zweifel aufkommen lassen, sind ohne besondere Erwähnung korrigiert worden; in unsicheren Fällen, habe ich es für notwendig gehalten, meine Wahl zu begründen. Solers musikalische Intentionen sind jedoch meistens vollkommen klar.

Eine kleine Anzahl offensichtlich unerläßlicher Verzierungen sind von Parallelpassagen abgeleitet und gesondert aufgeführt worden und können leicht als Anmerkungen in den Text gesetzt werden, wenn dem Spieler dies notwendig erscheint. Hier und da sind Noten, Bindungen, Bindezeichen und Vorzeichen eingefügt worden, wo anhand von früheren Parallelpassagen bewiesen ist, daß sie offensichtlich fehlen; diese sind mit dem üblichen wissenschaftlichen Apparat kenntlich gemacht. Ich habe mich durchweg bemüht, einen möglichst klaren, spielfertigen Text zu präsentieren, ohne visuelle Hindernisse durch Herausgebereingriffe in Form von Klammern, markierten Bindebögen und Bindungen und ähnlichen Dingen, die den Spieler leicht ablenken können. Deshalb brauchen die Herausgeberanmerkungen nur einmal, mit dem Bleistift in der Hand, für jede Sonate entschlüsselt zu werden.

Ich habe den Syndikussen des Fitzwilliam Museums in Cambridge zu danken für die Genehmigung, diese Anthologie von ihrer Kopie des Originaldrucks zu veröffentlichen.

Chartres, 1986   KENNETH GILBERT

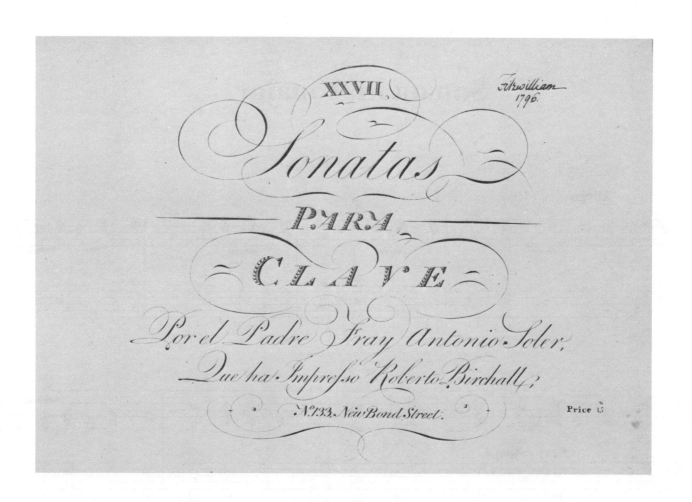

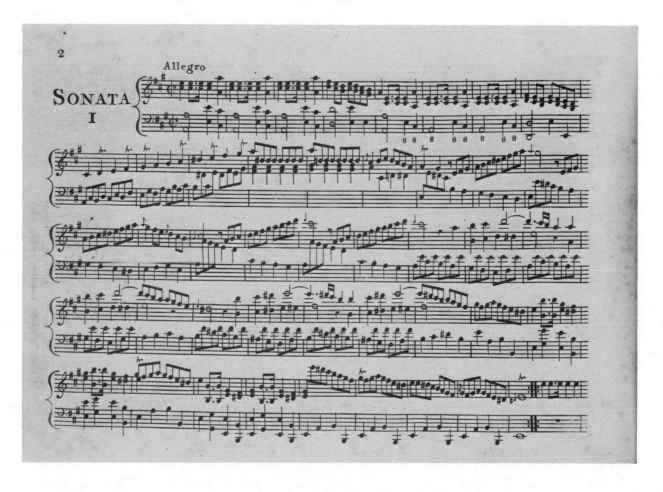

Sonata in A major

4

Sonata in G major

8

mutandi i deti

Sonata in C major

Sonata in C major

Sonata in B major

Andantino

Sonata in E♭ major

Largo andante

29

Sonata in C minor

Sonata in C minor

Allegro moderato

Sonata in C♯ minor

Sonata in C♯ minor

★ See Editorial notes

Sonata in D minor

Sonata in D minor

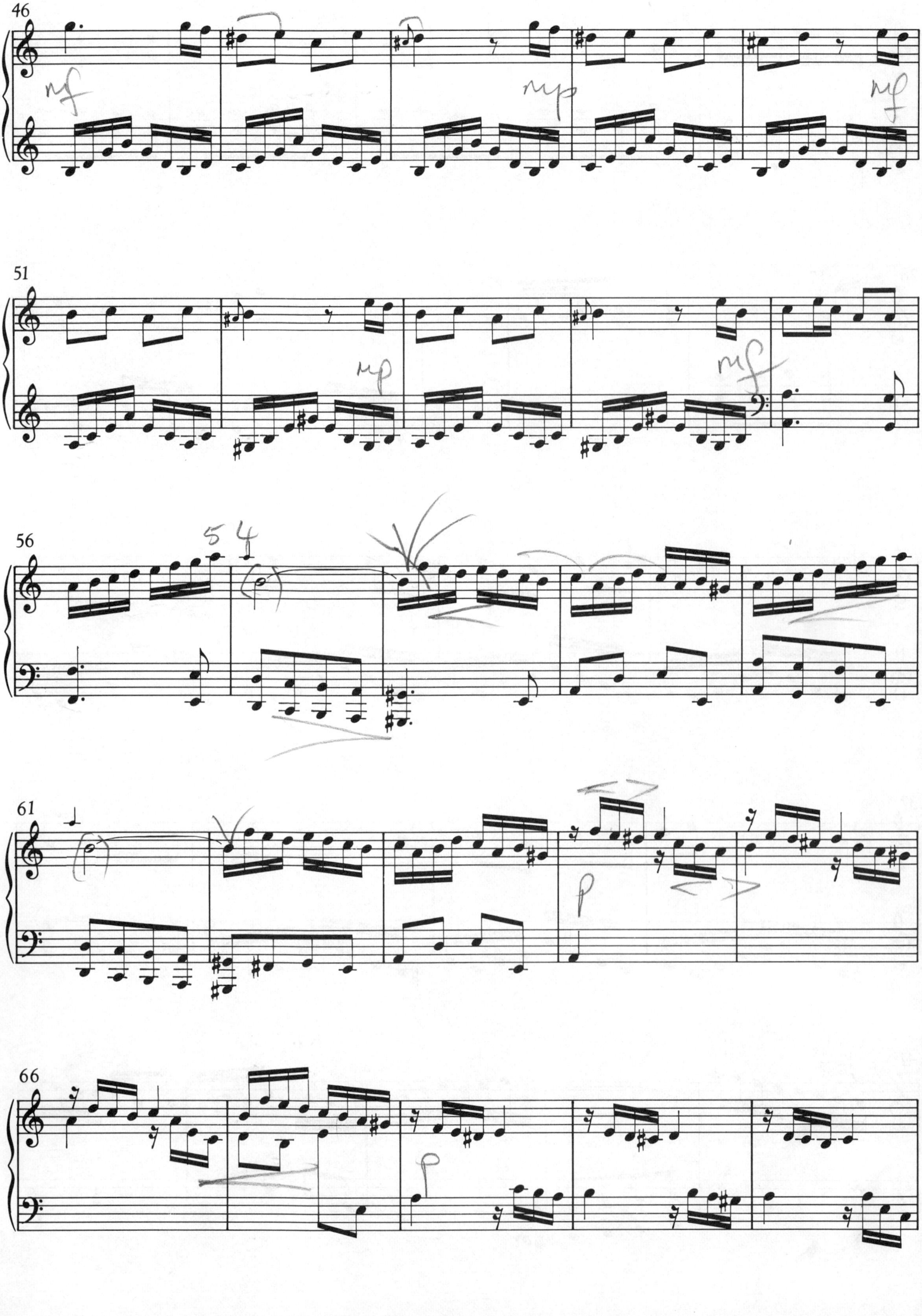
46
51
56
61
66

Sonata in E minor

Sonata in E minor

EDITORIAL NOTES

Roman numbers in square brackets are from Birchall's edition. (For the 27 Fitzwilliam sonatas these are identical to the numbers in Rubio's collected edition.)

Abbreviations: acc = accidental   m = missing   R = right hand   L = left hand

10 R 2 *means* bar 10, right hand, 2nd note.

1. SONATA IN A MAJOR [I]
   10 R 2: *tr* on previous note
   13 R 1: *A* for *B*
   16 L 4: acc m
   24 R 3: lower note of octave m
   25 L 7: *F* for *G*
   37: identical to 39
   53 R 2: ♯ on previous note
   60 L 1st chord: bass note *F* for *G*♮; becomes *G*♮ on 2nd beat

2. SONATA IN G MAJOR [IV]
   15 R 2: *D* for *C*
   34: 1st- and 2nd-time bars condensed into a single bar, but the intention is clear
   37 R 3: acc m
   37 L 2, 3: *E, F* in octaves (engraving error based on bar 39; see bar 35)
   tr added: R bar 47

3. SONATA IN C MAJOR [VIII]
   13, 17, 27, 118, 122, 128 L: the ties have been added from the correct pattern found in bar 31
   26 R: *B* m
   39 L 3: there is an *F*♯ above the *D*
   41 R 2, 3: undotted semiquavers
   100 R 1: alto *G* m
   100, 101, 103 R: ties m
   116, 117, 120–122 R: acc m
   119, 129 L: m
   136–143, 149–156 R: alto *G* m
   153: *p* m
   156 R: alto *G* m
   182 R: alto *E* for *D*
   tr added: R bars 135, 169, 172

4. SONATA IN C MAJOR [IX]
   89–90, 93–94, 124–125 L: slurs added
   129 R: slur added
   138: this bar is missing (see bar 65)
   tr added: R bar 32

5. SONATA IN B MAJOR [XI]
   10 R 4: crotchet
   15 R 5: *A* for *B*
   24 R 3: *A* for *G*
   28 R 5: acc m
   72 L 1: acc m
   74 L 1: chord is *E*♮, *G, A*♮, *C*
   74 L 2, 74 R 3: acc m
   82, 84, 86, 88 R: tie m
   84 R 4: appoggiatura m

112 R last chord: *B, D* for *A, C*
tr added: R bars 24, 71, 73, 91, 97, 103, 110

6. SONATA IN E♭ MAJOR [XVI]
   Numerous missing ties have been added from parallel passages
   2 L 1: *A* for *B*
   18 R: alto *F* m
   64 R 2, 3: the alto figure is dotted only on this, its first occurrence; the dotting, which should of course be maintained throughout the rest of the piece, affords a useful clue to the correct tempo
   87 R 2nd beat: chord is *E*♮, *G*♮, *B*(♭)
   99 R 1: alto *F* m
   tr added: R bars 11, 37, 39, 59, 60, 86, 87, 95, 100, 110, 125; L bar 6

7. SONATA IN C MINOR [XVIII]
   20, 22 R: acc m
   20 L 3: *D* for *F*
   46 R 2, 3: *C, E* for *D, G*
   48 R 2: *C* for *D*
   tr added: R bar 44 (2nd)

8. SONATA IN C MINOR [XIX]
   13 L 5: *B* for *C*
   16–19: ties m
   17 R 10, 11: *A, B* for *B, A*
   28 L 1: acc m
   32 L 2nd beat: bass *B* m
   53, 54 L: tie m
   57 L 2nd beat: alto *B* m
   60, 61 R 3–6: alto part m
   65 R 1: acc m
   65 R 3: *E*♮
   66, 67 R: the high *G* is mistakenly notated as *E* (one leger line missing)
   69 R 12: ♭ for ♮ (see bar 63)
   tr added: R bar 30

9. SONATA IN C♯ MINOR [XX]
   2, 6 L: tie m
   13, 28, 96, 100 R: tie m
   26, 34, 36 L 2nd beat: alto *F, G* m
   39 L 1: acc m
   49 L 1: *F* for *A*
   53 L 1, 2: alto 2 semiquavers
   58, 59 L 1, 2: the middle part is, here only, notated as dotted semiquaver, demisemiquaver; this seems a more plausible rhythmic figure for the left hand and, allowing for an initial engraving error, might possibly have been intended for similar figures throughout the piece
   59 L 2nd beat: acc m before bass *D*

60 R last note: acc m
76 R: tie m
81, 90 R: appoggiatura is crotchet
83 L 2: bass *G* m
94–95, 98–99 R: accs m
102, 103 R 2nd beat: 1st lower stem on *F* is semiquaver
tr added: R bars 22, 32, 80

10. SONATA IN C♯ MINOR [XXI]
   Numerous missing ties have been added from parallel passages
   26 R 5, 6: last two lower notes *D, E* for *E, D*
   43 R 1, 2: *B♯, A* for *A♯, G*
   49 R 6: ✗ m, as in many other instances throughout the sonata
   99 R 2: acc m
   106: the editor recommends the insertion here of three bars based
       on 113–115 (the leap of a 7th in the R is highly unlikely:
       Birchall's engraver probably missed these three bars)
   127 L: upper note of octave m
   tr added: R bars 17, 19, 68

11. SONATA IN D MINOR [XXIV]
   Numerous missing ties have been added from parallel passages
   12 R 2, 3: *F, G* m
   16 R 3: *D* for *E*
   18 R: alto part m
   41: this bar could be redundant (see bars 30–36), but could
       equally be the result of a characteristic expansion of the phrase
       from six into seven bars
   59: key-signature change m
   117 L 3: bass *F* for *G*
   142 L: acc m
   150 L: bass m
   168 R 1: acc m
   202, 210: no ♯ before small *G*
   tr added: R bars 5, 6, 14, 48, 181; L bars 60, 61, 181, 195

12. SONATA IN D MINOR [XXV]
   8–10 R: ties across barlines m
   29 L: tie m
   29–30: no barline
   39, 54 R last note: could be *D* (see bars 113, 128)
   78 R 2nd beat: alto quaver, two semiquavers
   92–97 R: alto part m
   139 R 3: acc m
   tr added: R bars 18, 76, 92 (both), 99, 101, 103

13. SONATA IN E MINOR [XXVI]
   23, 31 R last note: acc m
   70 R small note: acc m
   71, 72 R: no ♯ before *D*s
   75, 76 R: tie m
   77 R: ♯ before *B*; small note m
   79 R: appoggiatura m
   88 R 7: acc m
   89 R 1: small *C* for *A♯*
   90, 91 R 1, 2: two undotted quavers
   96 L 1: *G* m
   103 L 4: acc m
   105 R: the eight notes are wrongly beamed as two groups of four
       quavers, but are also correctly aligned as in 109
   108 L: *G, A, B, G* for *E, F, G, E*
   tr added: R bars 8, 30 (both), 56, 88 (both), 96 (both), 117, 119

14. SONATA IN E MINOR [XXVII]
   1 R 4, 2 L 4: acc m
   16 R: tie m
   36, 50 R 1: *C* below *E*
   54 R 1: alto *C* m
   91 R 1: ♯ for ♮
   98, 103 L 4: acc m
   tr added: R bars 116, 118